AVENGERS VS. ULTRON

WRITERS: **ROY THOMAS, DAVID MICHELINIE, JEFF PARKER, CLAY MCLEOD CHAPMAN & CHRIS GIARRUSSO**

PENCILERS: **JOHN BUSCEMA, GEORGE PÉREZ, REILLY BROWN, MANUEL GARCIA, LUCIANO VECCHIO & CHRIS GIARRUSSO**

INKERS: **GEORGE KLEIN, MIKE ESPOSITO, PAT DAVIDSON, SCOTT KOBLISH, LUCIANO VECCHIO & CHRIS GIARRUSSO**

COLORISTS: **DON WARFIELD, CHRISTINA STRAIN, VAL STAPLES, SOTOCOLOR & CHRIS GIARRUSSO**

LETTERERS: **SAM ROSEN, JOHN COSTANZA, DAVE LANPHEAR, DAVE SHARPE, VC'S CLAYTON COWLES & CHRIS GIARRUSSO**

EDITORS: **STAN LEE, JIM SALICRUP, JOHN BARBER, MARK PANICCIA & TOM BRENNAN**

AVENGERS CREATED BY **STAN LEE & JACK KIRBY**

Collection Editor: **ALEX STARBUCK**
Assistant Editor: **SARAH BRUNSTAD**
Editors, Special Projects: **JENNIFER GRÜNWALD & MARK D. BEAZLEY**
Senior Editor, Special Projects: **JEFF YOUNGQUIST**
Research: **JACOB ROUGEMONT**
SVP Print, Sales & Marketing: **DAVID GABRIEL**
Book Design: **NELSON RIBEIRO**

Editor in Chief: **AXEL ALONSO**
Chief Creative Officer: **JOE QUESADA**
Publisher: **DAN BUCKLEY**
Executive Producer: **ALAN FINE**

Special Thanks to Jess Harrold

TABLE OF CONTENTS

The greatest foe Earth's Mightiest Heroes have ever faced is ready to be unleashed on an unsuspecting world in the blockbuster film Avengers: Age of Ultron — but you can get the inside scoop on the maniacal machine with this collection of Ultron's greatest hits! And we do mean hits, as the Adamantium antagonist gets in plenty of licks!

ULTRON — EARTH'S MIGHTIEST HERO?
"THE REPLACEMENTS"
MARVEL ADVENTURES THE AVENGERS #1

Move over, Avengers — the world doesn't need you any more. Not now that it has the Ultimate Robot Offender Neutralizer — let's call it Ultron for short! Oh, wait, that doesn't sound good. Tell you what, guys, you just stand by to save the day when the Ultron 700 Global Defense System inevitably goes horribly wrong, how about that? Thanks!

THE ROBOT AND THE ROGUES' GALLERY!
"THE MASTERS OF EVIL"
MARVEL ADVENTURES THE AVENGERS #4

The Avengers have a hard enough time defeating Ultron on his own — imagine if he joined a band of big bads so beastly they have a volcano base! Uh-oh, that's exactly what happens! Can even an awesome new lineup including Storm, Spider-Man, Giant-Girl and Wolverine hope to stop the Masters of Evil? We're talking Baron Zemo, the Leader, the Abomination and, oh yeah, Ultron!

VISION IMPAIRED!
"BABY STEPS"
MARVEL UNIVERSE AVENGERS EARTH'S MIGHTIEST HEROES #10

As Vision enjoys a day out, experiencing life as a human being in a special body cooked up by Tony Stark, Ultron decides to take the android Avenger's empty shell for a spin! Can Vision regain control of himself before Ultron unleashes animated annihilation on the rest of the team? And if he does, what will he have to sacrifice? Oh the humanity!

MINI MARVELS, MIGHTY MIRTH!
"THE IRON AVENGERS"
MINI MARVELS: THE COMPLETE COLLECTION GN-TPB

They're the Avengers you know and love, in adorable miniature! Brace yourself for side-splitting adventures from Earth's Wittiest Heroes, courtesy of the cartoonist who's as funny as his surname is hard to spell, Chris Giarrusso! When Iron Man makes armored suits for all his teammates, the cutest Ultron you ever saw seizes his moment to strike! But he didn't count on an animal Avenger...

ULTRON

THE AVENGERS

THE NEW MASTERS OF EVIL!

Ultron first appeared in **Avengers #54** (July 1968)

A founding member of the Avengers, the brilliant Hank Pym used his astounding intellect to design a robot based on his own brain patterns. Though the creation known as Ultron was activated with the best of intentions, even Pym's genius could not have predicted that his robot would immediately rebel, becoming a threat to all humanity. Ultron's obsession with destroying his "father" would lead him to challenge the Avengers on many occasions. Though he has been unsuccessful thus far, Ultron's ability to continuously recreate himself in newer and more powerful forms makes him a formidable foe and a constant thorn in the sides of Earth's Mightiest Heroes!

ANNIHILATION CONQUEST

MARVEL
5 of 6

Ultron unites with the Phalanx in **Annihilation: Conquest #5** (May 2008)

Height: 6' (variable)
Weight: 535 lbs. (variable)

Power and Weapons:
Ultron's outer shell is usually composed of Adamantium, rendering it almost totally impervious to damage. However, his internal mechanisms are generally less durable and more easily damaged. His skin composition is about half an inch thick; neck, knee, ankle, elbow, shoulder, wrist and finger joints are a finely tessellated titanium alloy to permit flexing. He is able to withstand concussive blasts and heat of a 100-megaton atomic bomb.

POWER GRID	0	1	2	3	4	5	6	7
INTELLIGENCE								
STRENGTH								
SPEED								
DURABILITY								
ENERGY PROJECTION								
FIGHTING SKILLS								

ULTRON

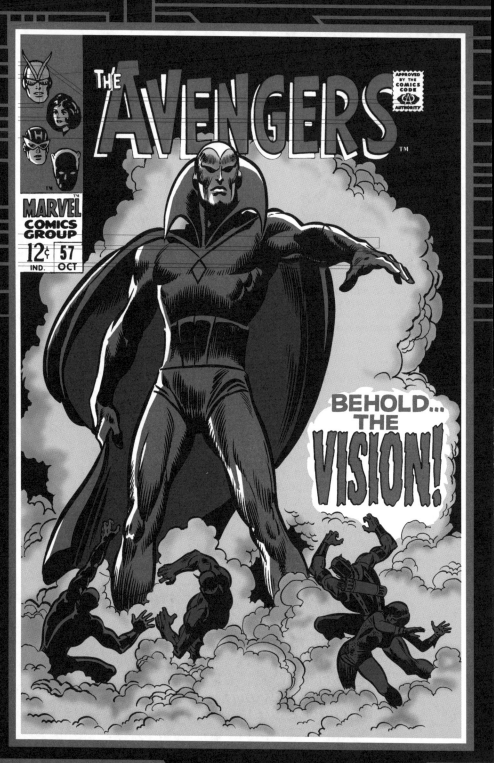

RAIN FALLS ON THE PARCHED CITY ...A RAIN THAT SENDS ALL SCURRYING FOR SHELTER...

ALL SAVE **ONE**, WHO STALKS ALONE THE CONCRETE CANYONS, HEEDLESS OF THE TORRENTIAL DOWNPOUR...

...BECAUSE IT DOES NOT **TOUCH** HIM...!

THEN, SILENTLY, EFFORTLESSLY ...LIKE SOME GREAT, VENGEFUL **BIRD OF PREY**...HE SWOOPS INTO THE MOONLESS, CLOUD-DRAPED SKY...TOWARDS A TOWERING STRUCTURE NEARBY...

"BEHOLD...THE **VISION!**"

AN EERIE EXPEDITION INTO UNEXPLORED REALMS, CONDUCTED BY: STAN LEE, EDITOR! ROY THOMAS, WRITER! JOHN BUSCEMA, ARTIST! GEORGE KLEIN, INKER! SAM ROSEN, LETTERER!

3.

8

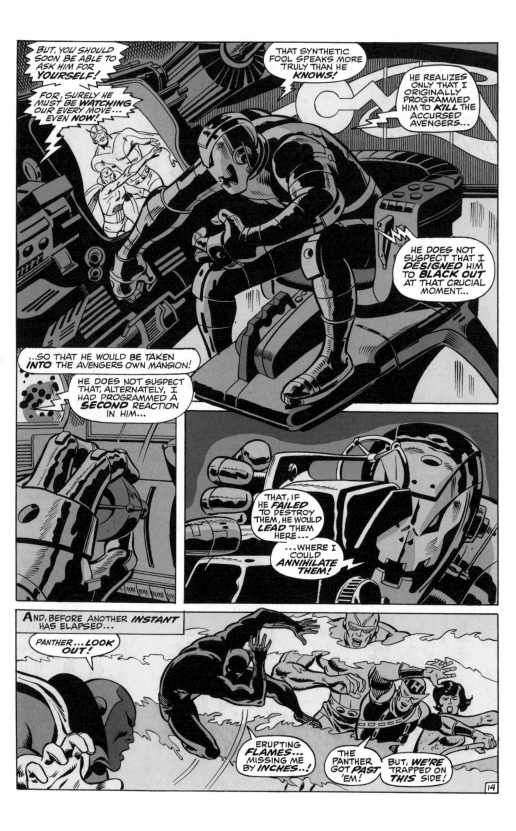

16

EPILOGUE:
I met a traveler from an antique land, Who said:

Two vast and trunkless legs of stone Stand in the desert.

Near them, on the sand, Half sunk, a shattered visage lies,

Whose frown, And wrinkled lip, and sneer of cold command,

Tell that its sculptor well those passions read Which yet survive, stamped on these lifeless things...

The hand that mocked them, and the heart that fed; And on the pedestal these words appear:

"My name is Ozymandias, King of Kings: Look on my works, ye Mighty, and despair!"

Nothing beside remains. Round the decay Of that colossal wreck, Boundless and bare

The lone and level sands stretch far away.

"BUT JUST BEFORE IT LET LOOSE WITH A POWER BLAST, I WAS ABLE TO SHRINK TO WASP-SIZE AND GET AWAY.

"I DIDN'T KNOW WHAT ELSE TO DO THEN, SO I FLEW ALL THE WAY OVER TO MANHATTAN FROM NEW JERSEY--

"--AND BY THE TIME I REACHED AVENGERS MANSION MY WINGS WERE SO TIRED THAT I COULD HARDLY STAY IN THE AIR. I LOST CONTROL, WAS HEADING STRAIGHT FOR A WINDOW--

"--SO I USED A BIO-POWER STING TO BREAK IT BEFORE I ENDED UP SQUASHED LIKE A BUG ON A CAR WINDSHIELD!"

YOU LOOK FINE, WASP.

GOLLY, I'LL BET MY HAIR IS JUST A MESS!

BUT THE ROBOT! WHAT ABOUT THE--

HOLD IT! DO YOU HEAR SOMETHING?

YEAH! LIKE A CLANKING SOUND COMIN' DOWN THE HALL!

CAPTAIN AMERICA, YOU DON'T THINK...?

I DON'T KNOW, WANDA, BUT WE'RE NOT TAKING ANY CHANCES! DEFENSIVE POSITIONS, EVERY-ONE!

IF THAT ROBOT DID FOLLOW JAN HERE, IT'S GOING TO GET A HEARTY RECEPTION!

THE OMINOUS RATTLING GROWS, GETTING CLOSER... UNTIL...

3

Panel 1: THAT'S RIGHT, WANDA. ULTRON HAS A UNIQUE MOLECULAR REARRANGER BUILT INTO HIS CHEST, ONE THAT ENABLES HIM TO ALTER HIS ADAMANTIUM FORM AT WILL. THE LAST TIME WE FOUGHT, THE RANDOM HEX YOU CAST CAUSED THAT REARRANGER TO MALFUNCTION, RESULTING IN ULTRON'S DEFEAT.

Panel 2: AND THAT MAKES YOU, IN ULTRON'S EYES, THE MOST DANGEROUS OF US ALL -- AND THE ONE HE'S MOST LIKELY TO STRIKE AT FIRST.

I AM ACCUSTOMED TO TAKING CARE OF MYSELF, CAPTAIN. WHY DON'T WE JUST LET JOCASTA TRACK ULTRON DOWN WITH HER CYBERNETIC SENSES? THEN WE COULD TAKE THE BATTLE TO HIM.

Panel 3: I'VE BEEN TRYING TO DO JUST THAT, WANDA -- AS WELL AS GET A FIX ON THE BEAST'S MUTANT ENERGY, TO BRING HIM AND WONDER MAN BACK TO AVENGERS MANSION -- *

* THEY LEFT TO TAPE A TV SHOW LAST ISSUE. -- Salicrup.

Panel 4: -- BUT MY SENSORY NETWORK IS MALFUNCTIONING, AS IF SOMETHING WERE JAMMING IT FROM AFAR!

THAT SOUNDS LIKE ULTRON, ALL RIGHT.

Panel 5: PERHAPS IT WOULD BE ACCEPTABLE TO ALL CONCERNED, CAPTAIN AMERICA, IF I WERE TO TAKE RESPONSIBILITY FOR MY WIFE'S SECURITY.

SOUNDS REASONABLE TO ME, VISION. WANDA?

WELLLL...

Panel 6: GOOD, THEN IT'S SETTLED. THE REST OF YOU ARE FREE TO GO ABOUT YOUR DUTIES, BUT STAY CLOSE --

-- AS OF RIGHT NOW, THE AVENGERS ARE ON YELLOW ALERT!

Panel 7: AND SOON...

HEY, WASP! JAN! WAIT UP!

YES, HAWKEYE?

Panel 8: LISTEN, UM, I JUST WANTED TO APOLOGIZE FOR THAT CRACK I MADE ABOUT HANK BACK THERE. I GUESS SOMETIMES MY MOUTH SAYS THINGS BEFORE MY MIND HAS A CHANCE TO EDIT THEM.

THAT'S OKAY, HAWKEYE. YOUR MOUTH MAY BE BIG -- BUT IT'S CUTE. YOU'RE FORGIVEN.

6

LATER, SUNRISE OVER MANHATTAN: A CRIMSON ORB SENDING EARLY LIGHT SPLASHING THROUGH THE HAZE OVER THE EAST RIVER--

--WARMING THE PRIVATE CHAMBERS OF THE HUSBAND-AND-WIFE AVENGERS KNOWN AS THE VISION AND THE SCARLET WITCH.

THE DAWN IS BEAUTIFUL, IS IT NOT, DARLING? DO YOU THINK IT WAS MEANT TO INSPIRE US?

ACTUALLY, WANDA, THE COLOR-ATION YOU REFER TO IS THE RESULT OF THE UNIQUE REFRACTIVE QUALITIES OF THE VARIOUS AIRBORNE POLLU-TANTS PRESENT IN THIS VICINITY.

WHA--?! BLAST IT, VISION! CAN'T YOU SEE THAT I'M LOOKING FOR A LITTLE TENDER-NESS? A LITTLE COMPASSION?

WHAT WOULD YOU HAVE ME DO, MY WIFE?

I'D HAVE YOU LET GO OF ME, THAT'S WHAT! IF YOU'RE SO BLAMED INSENSITIVE THAT YOU CAN'T TELL WHEN YOUR OWN WIFE NEEDS COMFORTING--

BUT I CANNOT LET YOU GO-- MY JOB IS TO PROTECT YOU. WOULD YOU LIKE ME TO LIST THE REFRACTIONAL INDICES OF THE CHEMICAL POLLU-TANTS NOW? PERHAPS IN DESCENDING ORDER?

YOU DO AND I'LL HEX YOU INTO PLASTIC SLAG, YOU COMPUTERIZED--

;--HLMGF?!?;

THE SCARLET WITCH RESISTS, BUT HER STRUGGLES EASE AS HER TENSION DRAINS. THE TEASING IS OVER.

AND THE COMFORT THAT THESE TWO WARRIORS AND LOVERS FIND IN EACH OTHER'S ARMS GIVES EVIDENCE THAT THE SUNRISE HAS, INDEED, INSPIRED THEM BOTH.

7

AND SO, SECONDS LATER, CARRYING THE UNCONSCIOUS FORM OF THE SCARLET WITCH IN HIS ARMS, AN UNUSUALLY ROBOTIC IRON MAN ROCKETS FROM AN UPPER-FLOOR WINDOW--

--ARCING BACK TO PAUSE BRIEFLY BEFORE A WINDOW WHERE THE AVENGERS' LOYAL BUTLER ENJOYS A RARE CATNAP BETWEEN DUTIES.

THERE, HE RAISES A GAUNTLETED FINGER--

--AND CYBERNETICALLY ACTIVATES A PENCIL-THIN LASER BEAM--

--TURNING WHAT COULD WELL BE THE MOST IMPORTANT ENVELOPE IN THE WORLD INTO A CLUSTER OF BLACKENED ASH AND SHATTERED HOPE.

THEN, LIKE A GLINTING, GOLDEN ARROW, IRON MAN STREAKS WESTWARD THROUGH THE MIDNIGHT SKY--

--COMING AT LAST TO NEVILLE ISLAND, AN UGLY SLAB OF MUD AND SHALE STUCK IN THE OCHER FLOW OF THE OHIO RIVER. ONCE IT HAD BEEN HOME TO THE DAVREAUX HEAVY METALS PLANT--

--NOW, IT IS HOME TO CAULDRONS OF BUBBLING, LASER-HEATED ADAMANTIUM... AND TO AN ENTITY WHOM FEW WOULD DENY AS BEING EVIL INCARNATE!

THAT WAS CLEVER, STARK-- CLOTHING YOURSELF IN IRON MAN ARMOR TO MOVE FREELY AMONGST THE AVENGERS. YOU'VE DONE WELL.

I...FEEL THE NEED... TO SERVE YOU... ULTRON.

YES, MY PSYCHO-HYPNOSIS HAS SEEN TO THAT. AND YOU ARE BUT THE FIRST... FOR SOON, ALL HUMANITY WILL SERVE ME.

THEY WILL SERVE...

...OR DIE!

13

THANK HEAVENS YOU'RE ALL STILL ALIVE! WHEN THE TRACER REACTIVATED, LOCKING ONTO IRON MAN'S POWER OUTPUT, WE JUST PRAYED THAT WE'D GET HERE IN TIME!

WHICH WE DID, YOU METAL MANIAC!

SHEESH! YA DON'T HAVE TO GET SO CHOKED UP ABOUT IT!

WHAMB

XHUNOOM

AN' THIS CONCUSSION ARROW'S JUST TO LET YOU KNOW THAT THE AVENGERS TAKE CARE O' THEIR OWN!

MY WIFE! ARE YOU...?

HOW ABOUT YOU, IRON MAN?

I'M WEAK, AND I'M HURT, BUT THAT'S NOT IMPORTANT. WE HAVE TO STOP ULTRON, HERE AND NOW! JUST BE CAREFUL OF THOSE VATS--

THERE SHALL BE LITTLE NEED OF CAUTION, MY FRIEND, IT'S A BATTLE THAT IS NIGH ENDED! FOR WHILE ULTRON HATH TRIUMPHED O'ER MORTAL WARRIORS, NOW HE DOTH FACE--

I'M FINE, VISION... NOW.

-- THEY'RE FILLED WITH LIQUID ADAMANTIUM!

19

"WHO KNOWS WHAT'S GOING TO BE CRUCIAL TO SOMEONE, MR. HANLON? THERE ARE STRANGER NEEDS THAN THE IDEA OF A MAN IN A RED COSTUME GLIDING OVER THE ROOFTOPS WITH A BAG OF GIFTS."

WHAT A DUNDERHEAD.

I CAN'T *BELIEVE* I FORGOT THAT THE AVENGERS' HOLIDAY PARTY WAS GOING TO BE AT *DR. STRANGE'S PLACE.* I THOUGHT I'D MEET MJ ON TIME AT STARK TOWER.

BOY, IS SHE GONNA READ ME THE RIOT ACT.

Yes, Virginia, There Is A
SANTRON

Story: Jeff Parker
Pencils: Reilly Brown
Inks: Pat Davidson
Letters: Dave Lanphear
Colors: Christina Strain
Assistant Editor: Nicole Wiley
Editor: John Barber
Consulting Editor: Ralph Macchio
Editor in Chief: Joe Quesada
Publisher: Dan Buckley

OH, IT WILL BE LOUD.

"I'VE BEEN HERE FOR 30 MINUTES WITH NO ONE TO TALK TO!"

"HOW COULD YOU LEAVE ME LIKE THIS!"

HI, WONG, GOOD TO SEE YOU AGAIN.

ENTER, WEBBED ONE.

COULD I GET YOU ANYTHING, MARY JANE?

SO WHEN DO YOU WANT ME TO KILL PARKER?

DID I MENTION THAT I'M RICH?

OR... MAYBE NOT.

WOW, *SPIDER-MAN* JUST WENT INSIDE! I'D LOVE TO HAVE A CHANCE TO TALK TO HIM AGAIN!

HI, THE NAME'S *GRAVITY.*

I'M ONE OF THE NEW GUYS, HEH...

I WAS TOLD I DIDN'T NEED AN--

CLICK

--INVITE.

"THE ULTRON NEURAL NET IS FULL OF IMAGERY FROM VIRGIE'S MIND. IT'S NOT HARD TO FOLLOW.

"AS A CHILD, CHRISTMAS WAS CLEARLY A HUGE DEAL TO VIRGIE. ALL-IMPORTANT. THERE'S TONS OF DATA LIKE THIS.

"WHEN SHE WAS EIGHT, SOME KIDS TOLD HER SANTA CLAUS WASN'T REAL...

"...AND SHE DIDN'T TAKE IT TOO WELL. FOR A LONG TIME SHE DIDN'T TALK TO ANYONE.

"SHE EVENTUALLY BECAME FUNCTIONAL AGAIN, BUT STILL KEPT OUT OF SOCIETY AT LARGE."

SHE'S BEEN PROTECTING HER-SELF FROM CONTRARY IDEAS EVER SINCE-- A CLASSIC DEFENSE MECHANISM.

WELL, SHE SURE PUT A LOT OF DEFENSE MECHANISMS INTO HER SANTA...HOW DID THAT HAPPEN?

"ULTRON ALWAYS KEEPS SPARE BODIES OF HIMSELF TO TRANSFER HIS MIND INTO IF HE'S DESTROYED. AFTER A BIG BLOWOUT WITH THE AVENGERS A WHILE BACK, HIS PROGRAMMING UPLOADED TO ITS NEXT VERSION, AND SOME OF THAT WENT INTO AN UNFINISHED PROTOTYPE.

"AS IT OFTEN DOES, THE UNIT SOUGHT OUT A MIND CAPABLE OF FINISHING IT, AND USED ITS ENCEPHALO-OVERRIDER TO CONTROL VIRGIE'S PSYCHE. OF COURSE, HER BRAIN WAS FRAGMENTED, YOU COULD SAY...AND MANAGED TO WORK IN ITS OWN AGENDA ALONG WITH ULTRON'S.

"WHEN SHE SAW THE GROUNDWORK FOR AN ANDROID COME TO HER, SHE TOOK IT AS PROVIDENCE. A CHANCE TO RIGHT THE GREATEST WRONG IN HER LIFE."

THE AVENGERS

#1

MARVEL ADVENTURES
THE AVENGERS

...ONE--

KATHOOOOOOMMM

"We can't stress enough how sorry we are to have put you through this."

Nor can we thank you enough for stopping Ultron.

That's the problem now, sir...

...as your own people said, Ultron can't really be destroyed.

He's spread his mind across the networks--probably already planning a new attack.

And its goal will still be to make the human race answer to machines.

Job security for us, at least.

Bet puny Banner taking Hulk's checks!

But...but... what will we do when it returns?

Whatcha always do when things go wrong big-time.

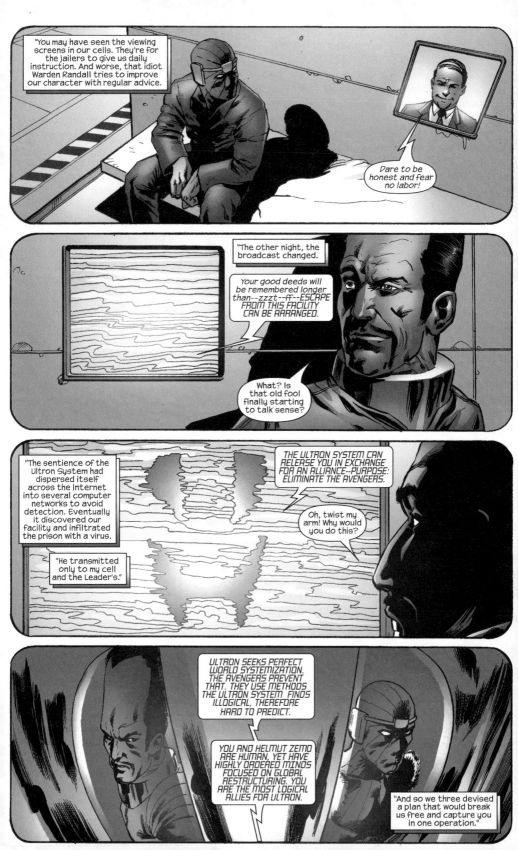

THE IRON AVENGERS

by **CHRIS GIARRUSSO**

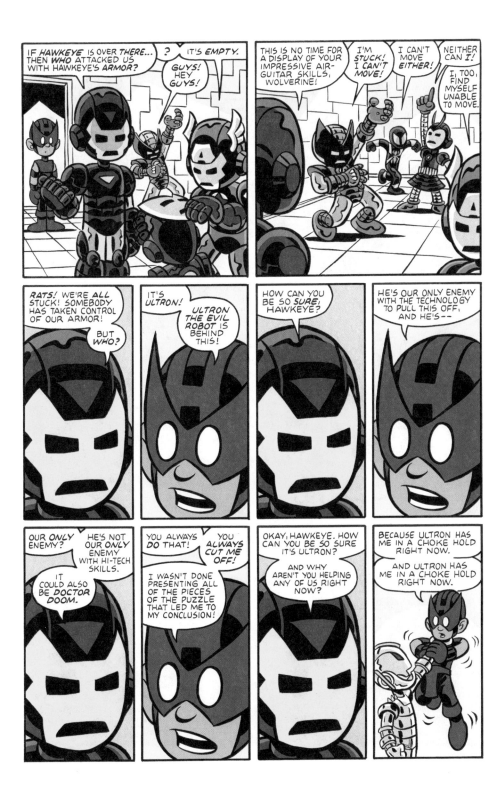